ADELE

BACK IN THE MIDDLE OF THE 20TH CENTURY WITH THE ADVENT OF A LITTLE INVENTION CALLED "TELEVISION" AND THE GROWING POPULARITY OF THE REBELLIOUSLY CONTROVERSIAL NEW STYLE OF MUSIC DUBBED "ROCK AND ROLL"...

FOUR BLOKES CALLED JOHN, PAUL, GEORGE, AND RINGO WERE AT THE FOREFRONT OF WHAT WAS KNOWN AS "THE BRITISH INVASION" WITH THEIR CATCHY TUNES, BOYISH GOOD LOOKS AND FREQUENT APPEARANCES ON THE WILDLY POPULAR "ED SULLIVAN SHOW." THEY WERE KNOWN AS THE BEATLES.

A YOUNG GIFTED SINGER NAMED ADELE WOULD BECOME PART OF ANOTHER WAVE OF A BRITISH INVASION SEVERAL YEARS LATER.

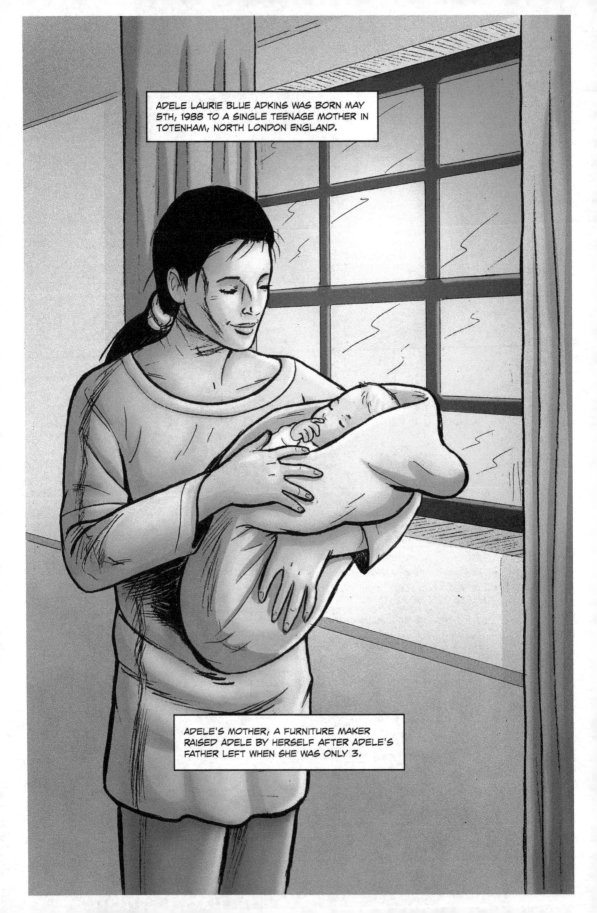

ADELE LAURIE BLUE ADKINS WAS BORN MAY 5TH, 1988 TO A SINGLE TEENAGE MOTHER IN TOTENHAM, NORTH LONDON ENGLAND.

ADELE'S MOTHER, A FURNITURE MAKER RAISED ADELE BY HERSELF AFTER ADELE'S FATHER LEFT WHEN SHE WAS ONLY 3.

WHILE COMING FROM A MOSTLY MUSIC-LESS FAMILY ADELE KNEW SHE WANTED TO SING FOR SURE AROUND THE AGE OF 14.

ADELE EVENTUALLY ATTENDED A SCHOOL OF PERFORMING ARTS.

WHILE SHE DOESN'T CONSIDER HERSELF A SOCIAL MEDIA STAR ONE OF ADELE'S FRIENDS WAS SAVVY ENOUGH TO PUT TOGETHER A MYSPACE PAGE FOR ADELE AT THE END OF 2004.

ADELE RELEASED HER FIRST ALBUM 19 TO MUCH CRITICAL ACCLAIM AND RECOGNITION FEATURING SUCH POWERFUL SONGS AS "HOMETOWN GLORY" AND "CHASING PAVEMENT".

ADELE 19

NO "SOPHOMORITIS" HERE, ADELE REALLY CAUGHT NOTICE WITH THE RELEASE OF HER SECOND ALBUM "21" DUE LARGELY IN PART TO THE UNDENIABLY ADDICTIVE SONG ROLLING IN THE DEEP.

IT CERTAINLY PROVED TO BE ADELE'S YEAR AND SHE CERTAINLY WAS IN DEMAND.

PART OF WHAT MAKES ADELE SO SPECIAL IS THE ONLY "GIMMICK" SHE OFFERS TO THE A.D.D. GENERATION IS NOTHING MORE THAN A POWERFUL VOICE THAT RESONATES WITH MANY PEOPLE TO THE TUNE OF 18 MILLION PLUS RECORDS SOLD, MULTIPLE AWARDS AND COUNTLESS ACCOLADES, DESPITE OFTEN BEING CRITICIZED FOR BOT BEING A SIZE ZERO.
IT'S NEVER BEEN AN ISSUE FOR ME - I DON'T WANT TO GO ON A DIET, I DON'T WANT TO EAT A CAESAR SALAD WITH NO DRESSING, WHY WOULD I DO THAT? I AIN'T GOT TIME FOR THIS, JUST BE HAPPY AND DON'T BE STUPID. IF I'VE GOT A BOYFRIEND AND HE LOVES MY BODY THEN I'M NOT WORRIED.

AT THE HEIGHT OF HER CAREER DURING WHAT WOULD BE DUBBED "ADELE'S YEAR" SHE HAD TO CANCEL SEVERAL PERFORMANCES DUE TO A HEMORRHAGE ON HER VOCAL CHORD.

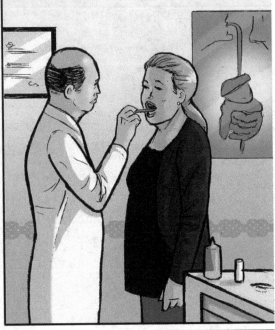

WOULD ADELE'S CAREER END AS QUICKLY AS IT HAD BEGUN?

DON'T CALL IT A COMEBACK! LUCKILY, WITH THE AID OF A SKILLED SURGEON ADELE'S SURGERY PROVED TO BE A SUCCESS AND HER VOICE WOULD BE RIGHT AS RAIN! LOOK OUT GRAMMY'S- HERE SHE COMES!

THE GRAMMY AWARDS, 2012, THE STAPLES CENTER LOS ANGELS, CA.

ADELE AND HER AMAZING VOICE MAKE A TRIUMPHANT RETURN TO THE LIVE STAGE PROVIDING A POWERFUL PERFORMANCE OF " ROLLING IN THE DEEP" TO A STANDING OVATION...

WHICH EVEN INCLUDED PERFORMING ATTENDEE LIVING LEGEND AND "BRITISH INVASION" PIONEER, PAUL MCCARTNEY.

SHE COULD HAVE HAD IT ALL AND SHE DID. ADELE KICKED OFF 2012 BY SWEEPING THE GRAMMYS BY WINNING SIX GRAMMYS IN ALL OF THE CATEGORIES.

WHAT'S NEXT FOR ADELE? A LOT OF TOURING FOR SURE . WILL SHE BE ABLE TO FOLLOW UP THE WORLD'S FAVORITE BREAK-UP ALBUM WITH A COLLECTION OF LOVE SONGS THAT HAVE THE SAME IMPACT AS 21?

AFTER ROLLING IN DEEP, SETTING FIRE TO THE RAIN AND FINDING SOMETHING LIKE SIX GRAMMY AWARDS ADELE IS SAID TO BE RETURNING TO THE STUDIO. HER FANS AND THE WORLD WAIT WITH BATED BREATH. IT ISN'T OVER. THE END. FOR NOW.

Ester S.

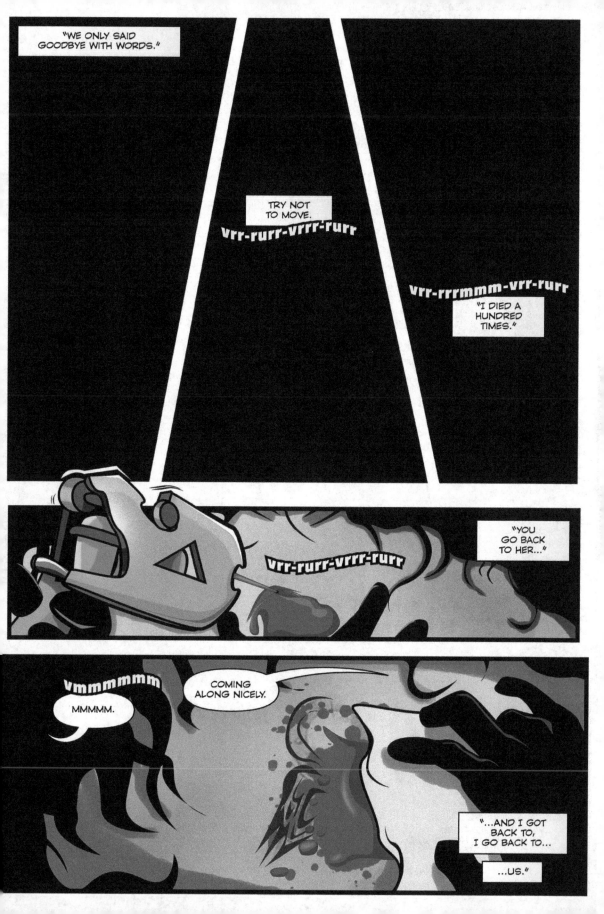

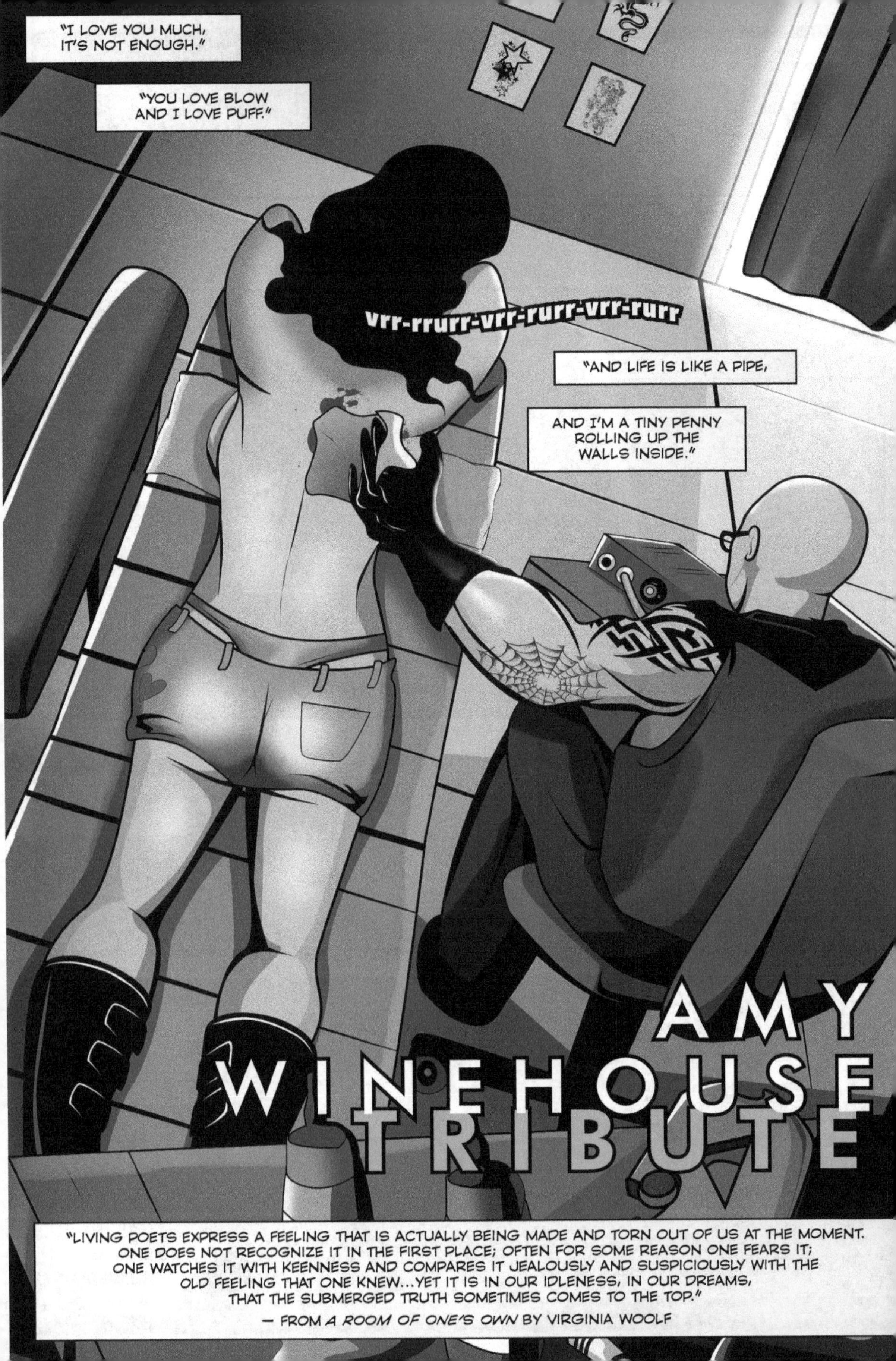
"I LOVE YOU MUCH, IT'S NOT ENOUGH."
"YOU LOVE BLOW AND I LOVE PUFF."
vrr-rrurr-vrr-rurr-vrr-rurr
"AND LIFE IS LIKE A PIPE,
AND I'M A TINY PENNY ROLLING UP THE WALLS INSIDE."
AMY WINEHOUSE TRIBUTE
"LIVING POETS EXPRESS A FEELING THAT IS ACTUALLY BEING MADE AND TORN OUT OF US AT THE MOMENT. ONE DOES NOT RECOGNIZE IT IN THE FIRST PLACE; OFTEN FOR SOME REASON ONE FEARS IT; ONE WATCHES IT WITH KEENNESS AND COMPARES IT JEALOUSLY AND SUSPICIOUSLY WITH THE OLD FEELING THAT ONE KNEW...YET IT IS IN OUR IDLENESS, IN OUR DREAMS, THAT THE SUBMERGED TRUTH SOMETIMES COMES TO THE TOP."
— FROM *A ROOM OF ONE'S OWN* BY VIRGINIA WOOLF

:GASP!:

...TO THE OFFICE! NOW!

SO YEAH, I HAVE A REBELLIOUS SIDE.

BUT I'VE HAD EVERYTHING PIERCED AT SOME POINT.

Principal and Head of Vocational Studies

...INTELLIGENT BUT UNFOCUSED... DOESN'T APPLY HERSELF... BRIGHT...REBELLIOUS...HANDFUL... ALWAYS MESSING ABOUT!

THEY EXPELLED ME WHEN I WAS 16.

ABOUT THE TIME YOU GOT YOUR FIRST TATTOO.

CLOSE. I WAS 15.

SHE'S HER OWN WOMAN, Y'KNOW?

I LIKE PIN-UP GIRLS. I'M MORE OF A BOY THAN A GIRL. I'M NOT A LESBIAN, THOUGH.

NO?

WELL...NOT BEFORE A SAMBUCA ANYWAY.

YOU READY?

THEN DOWN.

SURE, HONEY. I WAS *BORN* READY.

vrr-rr-rrurr-vrrr

THE TATTOO'S MARK *MILESTONES.* I GOT EXPELLED, BUT NOT BEFORE I MET TYLER JAMES, WHO PASSED ON MY DEMO TAPE TO HIS A & R REP.

A & R RECORDS WERE LOOKING FOR A JAZZ VOCALIST. THIS OPPORTUNITY LANDED ME A RECORDING CONTRACT WITH *ISLAND RECORDS,* THE MOST PRESTIGIOUS RECORD LABEL IN BRITAIN.

I WAS 20 WHEN *"FRANK,"* MY FIRST ALBUM, WAS RELEASED. IT WAS 2003.

THAT'S WHEN... THE DRINKING STARTED?

NOT GONNA DEFEND IT. MY JUSTIFICATION IS THAT MOST PEOPLE MY AGE SPEND A LOT OF TIME THINKING ABOUT WHAT THEY'RE GOING TO DO FOR THE NEXT FIVE OR TEN YEARS.

THE TIME THEY SPEND THINKING ABOUT THEIR LIFE, I JUST SPEND *DRINKING.*

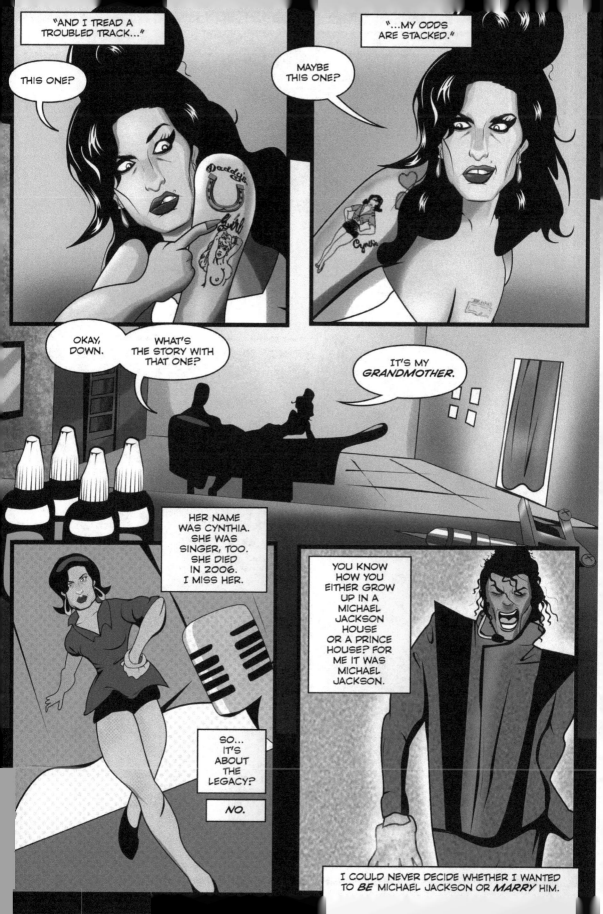

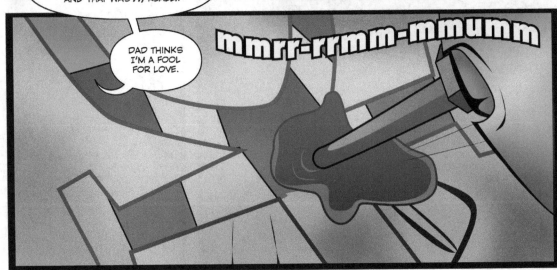

"*BACK IN BLACK*, THE NEW ALBUM BY AMY WINEHOUSE, HAS SKYROCKETED TO THE TOP OF THE UK CHARTS. RELEASED ON OCTOBER 30, 2006, WINEHOUSE CONQUERED THE CHARTS IN NORWAY, FINLAND, IRELAND, AND THE NETHERLANDS. THE ALBUM DOMINATED IN CANADA AND AUSTRALIA, AND IS NOW POISED TO TAKE THE TOP SPOT IN THE US. IT'S FIRST SINGLE, 'REHAB,' IS ALREADY ENJOYING MASSIVE AIRPLAY."

WHAT ABOUT *THAT* ONE? BESIDES THE OBVIOUS, WHAT IS ITS SPECIAL MEANING?

WHAT ONE?

Rrrr-vrrr-rrurr

THE HORSESHOE.

COLOR'S HOLDING NICE.

GOOD. IT MEANS MY DADDY IS MY GOOD LUCK CHARM.

IT'S CLEAR HE LOVES ME. HE'S PROTECTIVE...

...NOT TO MENTION THE *INTERVENTIONS*.

AROUND 3:30 A.M. THURSDAY, GUESTS OF THE SANDERSON HOTEL IN LONDON WERE SHOCKED TO SEE *AMY WINEHOUSE*, WHOSE ALBUM "BACK IN BLACK" GARNERED HER FIVE GRAMMY AWARDS, SPRINTING DOWN THE HALLWAY.

HER HUSBAND, BLAKE FIEDLER-CIVIL, WAS SEEN SPRINTING AFTER HER. BOTH RECEIVED MULTIPLE CUTS AND ABRASIONS IN WHAT APPEARS TO BE AN ALTERCATION IN HER HOTEL ROOM.

"IN A SERIES OF TEXTS TO BLOGGER PEREZ HILTON, MISS WINEHOUSE STATED, "BLAKE IS THE BEST MAN IN THE WORLD. WE WOULD NEVER HARM EACH OTHER. I WAS CUTTING MYSELF AFTER HE FOUND ME IN OUR ROOM ABOUT TO DO DRUGS WITH A CALL GIRL AND SAID I WASN'T GOOD ENOUGH FOR HIM. I LOST IT AND HE SAVED MY LIFE."

MY HUSBAND IS EVERYTHING TO ME AND WITHOUT HIM IT'S JUST NOT THE SAME. HE'S THE INSPIRATION FOR *BACK IN BLACK'S* LYRICS.

I...SEE. SO THE FIGHTING?

HE WAS SAVING MY LIFE. BUT I CAN BE A CRUEL PERSON.

AND THE OTHER...RUMORS... ABOUT YOUR *WEIGHT?* DID HE CONTRIBUTE TO THAT, TOO?

NO. I'M JUST UGLY.

NO. YOU'RE NOT.

SOME PEOPLE RECKONED THAT I LOOKED HEALTHIER WHEN I WAS BIGGER BUT I HAD TERRIBLE SKIN AND NO ENERGY.

I'M FINE.

WANT TO TAKE A *LOOK?*

YES!

AS USUAL, TREAT IT WITH LOTION EVERY FEW HOURS.

RIGHT.

WHY AN EGYPTIAN HIEROGLYPH WITH AMERICAN COLORS?

THE *ANKH* IS THE SYMBOL FOR ETERNAL LIFE. IT'S BEAUTIFUL WORK, REALLY.

THANK YOU. AND CELEBRITIES LIKE DENNIS RODMAN, SHAQUILLE O'NEAL AND ERYKAH BADUH SPORT ONE. BUT THE COLORS?

HERE IN ENGLAND, EVERYONE'S A *POP STAR,* INNIT?

WHEREAS IN AMERICA THEY BELIEVE IN THE TERM *"ARTIST."*

AND THE WINGS...?

A FLIGHT OF *FANCY.*

TATTOOS ALWAYS BUILD MY *CONFIDENCE.*

AND THIS ONE?

SYMBOLIZES COURAGE AND BRAVERY.

BRAVERY? YOU'RE THE BRAVEST PERSON I KNOW.

"THE MAN SAID, 'WHY DO YOU THINK YOU'RE HERE?' I SAID, 'I GOT NO IDEA I'M GONNA, I'M GONNA LOSE MY BABY SO I ALWAYS KEEP A BOTTLE NEAR.'"

I BELIEVE IN FATE AND I BELIEVE THAT THINGS HAPPEN FOR A REASON BUT I DON'T THINK THERE'S A HIGH POWER, NECESSARILY, SO SYMBOLS MAKE SENSE.

I BELIEVE IN *KARMA* VERY MUCH, THOUGH.

"HE SAID, 'I JUST THINK YOU'RE DEPRESSED, KISS ME, YEAH BABY, AND GO REST.'"

SO...YOU DON'T *PRAY?*

THE MINUTE I EVEN START TO THINK ABOUT...WHAT I'M DOING... I JUST *LOSE* IT. I HAVE TO SHUT MY EYES AND *FLOW.*

"THEY TRIED TO MAKE ME GO TO REHAB BUT I SAID, 'NO, NO, NO.' YES, I'VE BEEN BLACK BUT WHEN I COME BACK YOU'LL KNOW, KNOW, KNOW."

IF YOU DON'T THROW YOURSELF INTO SOMETHING, YOU'LL NEVER KNOW WHAT YOU *COULD* HAVE HAD.

THINK YOU'LL GET ANOTHER TATTOO?

"I DON'T EVER WANNA DRINK AGAIN I JUST, OOH, I JUST NEED A FRIEND I'M NOT GONNA SPEND TEN WEEKS HAVE EVERYONE THINK I'M ON THE MEND"

SURE. PROBABLY A DOVE. ON MY NECK.

"IT'S NOT JUST MY PRIDE."

A DOVE? WHY A DOVE?

"IT'S JUST 'TIL THESE TEARS HAVE DRIED."

AMY JADE WINEHOUSE (1983-2011)

IT MEANS I'M FREE.

BONO

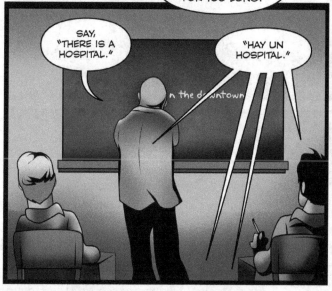

IT'S...YOUR *FATHER*...

...PREPAREST A TABLE BEFORE ME IN THE PRESENCE OF MINE ENEMIES: THOU ANOINTEST MY HEAD WITH OIL; MY CUP RUNNETH OVER.

...MOM?

SURELY GOODNESS AND MERCY SHALL FOLLOW ME ALL THE DAYS OF MY LIFE:

...BOBBY...I... I DON'T...FEEL...

I WILL DWELL IN THE HOUSE OF THE LORD...

"DUBLIN'S GONE ARSEWAYS. BOMBINGS. IT'S BANJAXED IS WHAT IT IS.

"PROTESTS. BOMBINGS. RELIGIOUS EXTREMISM. THE STREET CORNERS OCCUPIED BY BRASSERS, WHILE BOWSIES ROAM, THIEVING AS DISENFRANCHISED YOUTH ARE WANT TO DO.

BOOK STORE

Talbot Street

ANTI APARTHEID

IT'S TIME FOR OUR NEW PARADIGM, MATES." FORMING "*LYPTON VILLAGE*," OUR OWN ARTISTIC RETREAT, OUR OWN PARALLEL REALITY, WILL BE A CRAIC!

SO, WE'RE GOIN' BY OUR NEW *NAMES* WHEN WE'RE TOGETHER, THEN?

RIGHT. INSTEAD OF FIONAN HANVEY, YOU'RE "GAVIN FRIDAY."

AND DEREK, YOU'RE "GUGGI."

WELL, WE'VE GOT A NAME FOR YOU TOO, MATE.

MOUNT TEMPLE COMPREHENSIVE SCHOOL: 1976

SO, IT'S JUST THE FIVE OF 'EM NOW, IS IT?

YEAH, THEY SETTLED ON THE FIVE OF 'EM AFTER WEEDIN' OUT IVAN AND PETER. BUT DIK'S LAST SHOW IS TOMORROW.

SCRREEEEUNNGG!

WHAT'RE THEY CALLIN' THEMSELVES, THEN?

FEEDBACK!

TERRIBLE NAME...

I'M KIDDIN'! THAT'S THEIR OLD NAME.

"THEY'RE 'THE HYPE' NOW.

PRESBYTERIAN CHURCH HALL, HOWTH, IRELAND: MARCH, 1978

"BUT THAT'S ABOUT TO CHANGE, TOO. THEY'VE GOT A *PLAN*, YOU SEE.

"DIK'S LEAVIN' FOR TRINITY COLLEGE, SO HE'LL CEREMONIOUSLY EXIT THE STAGE.

"AND, WHEN HE DOES, THEY'LL HAVE A NEW NAME AND NEW MATERIAL INSTEAD OF COVERING SIOUXIE AND THE BANSHEES OR JOY DIVISION SONGS.

"U2."

LIMERICK, IRELAND:
SAINT PATRICK'S DAY, 1978

Four Dublin
schoolboys
carried off the
top prize at the
Limerick Civic
Week Pop '78
Competition on
Saturday night.

Sponsored by The Evening Press
and Harp Lager Guinness,
the competition was to find the
most talented and entertaining
pop group or showband.

The Dublin boys who attend
Mount Temple Comprehensive,
and are known as U2 Malahide,
headed 36 groups from all over the
country and won for themselves
£500, plus a trophy and a chance
to cut a demo for...

"IT'S ABOUT THE MESSAGE *WITHIN* THE MUSIC.
I HAVE A DREAM TODAY...
THAT ONE DAY... LITTLE BLACK BOYS AND BLACK GIRLS WILL BE ABLE TO JOIN HANDS WITH LITTLE WHITE BOYS AND LITTLE WHITE GIRLS AS SISTERS AND BROTHERS.
LIVE AID, JULY 1985: PERFORMANCE OF "PRIDE (IN THE NAME OF LOVE)"
I HAVE A *DREAM...*
"IN THE NAME... OF LOVE..."
"MAKE PEOPLE STOP AND CONSIDER EXACTLY WHAT'S GOING ON AROUND THEM."
"BONO, I JUST... CAN I CALL YOU BONO?

OF COURSE.

YOUR PUBLIC IMAGE AND PERSONAL BELIEFS SEEM TO BE THE SOURCE OF MUCH PRESS. HOW DO YOU FEEL ABOUT THIS SEEMING DICHOTOMY?

...SEEMING DICHOT—...? AH, BECAUSE I'M A ROCK STAR. WELL, LIFE'S ABOUT DUELING NATURES, ISN'T IT?

ESSENTIALLY, I'M A VERY REAL PERSON; GOOD *AND* BAD.

AND THE PUBLIC IMAGE IS ONE OF BEING VERY GOOD, I SUPPOSE. BUT ONE OF THE REASONS I'M *ATTRACTED* TO PEOPLE LIKE MARTIN LUTHER KING, JR., GANDHI, CHRIST, TO PACIFISM, IS BECAUSE NATURALLY,

I'M THE GUY THAT WOULD *NOT* TURN THE OTHER CHEEK — BUT,

"WHEN PEOPLE SEE YOU'RE ATTRACTED TO THAT, THEY THINK YOU *ARE* THAT."

What will it takes?

AN ECONOMIC RECESSION DOESN'T *HAVE* TO BE A *MORAL* RECESSION.

aftermath of war

give aid

Poverty

hunger

suffering

WE KNOW THERE ARE GOING TO BE CUTS... BUT *NOT* COSTS THAT ADD TO AIDS-RELATED DEATHS.

WORLD BANK: NOVEMBER, 2012

PRIME MINISTER, SOME OF THE CRIMINALS AROUND HERE ARE NOT WEARING SKI MASKS, THEY ARE WEARING *SKIS*.

WORLD ECONOMIC FORUM

BONO

WORLD ECONOMIC FORUM: DAVOS PANEL CHAIRED BY DAVID CAMERON, JANUARY 2014

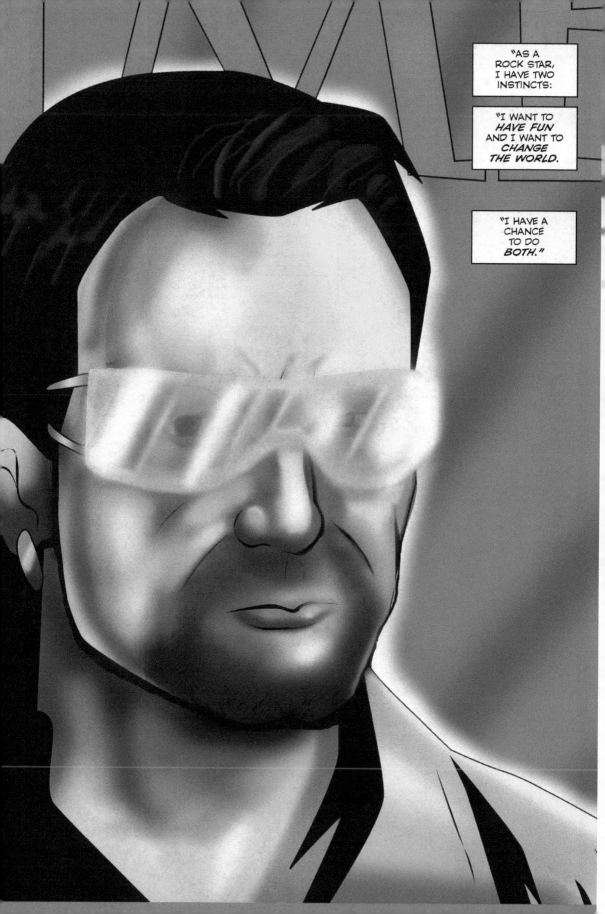

"OVERCOMING MY DAD TELLING ME THAT I COULD NEVER AMOUNT TO ANYTHING HAS MADE ME THE MEGALOMANIAC THAT YOU SEE TODAY.
PERSON OF THE YEAR
TIME
"MUSIC CAN CHANGE THE WORLD BECAUSE IT CAN CHANGE *PEOPLE.*"
THE GOOD SAMARITAN
BONO
FAME:
BONO

IT ALL BEGAN IN MID 80S, A SUB GENRE OF ALTERNATIVE ROCK, EMERGED FROM AMERICAN STATE OF WASHINGTON, SEATTLE, INSPIRED BY HARDCORE PUNK, HEAVY METAL AND ALTERNATIVE ROCK.
THE MUSIC GENRE WIDELY KNOWN AS *GRUNGE* BECAME COMMERCIALLY SUCCESS.
IT ALL START IN 1985 WHEN *KURT DONALD COBAIN* FORMED THE BAND *NIRVANA* WITH *KRIST NOVOSELIC*.

GRUNGE IS THE SOUND OF SEATTLE

GRUNGE IS GENERALLY CHARACTERIZED BY A SLUDGY GUITAR SOUND THAT USES A HIGH LEVEL OF DISTORTION, FUZZ AND FEEDBACK EFFECTS. GRUNGE FUSES ELEMENTS OF HARD-CORE PUNK AND HEAVY METAL, ALTHOUGH SOME BANDS PERFORMED WITH MORE EMPHASIS ON ONE OR THE OTHER. THE MUSIC SHARES WITH PUNK A RAW SOUND AND SIMILAR LYRICAL CONCERNS.

NIRVANA ESTABLISHED ITSELF AS PART OF THE SEATTLE GRUNGE SCENE, RELEASING ITS FIRST ALBUM BLEACH FOR THE INDEPENDENT RECORD LABEL SUB POP IN 1989. THE BAND EVENTUALLY CAME TO DEVELOP A SOUND THAT RELIED ON DYNAMIC CONTRASTS, OFTEN BETWEEN QUIET VERSES AND LOUD, HEAVY CHORUSES.

NIRVANA WAS SOON BEING CONSIDERED THE "FLAGSHIP BAND" OF GENERATION X. KURT COBAIN INTRODUCES ALTERNATIVE MUSIC THROUGH NIRVANA. WITHOUT NIRVANA, THERE MIGHT NOT BE BANDS LIKE ALICE IN CHAINS AND SOUNDGARDEN.

IT STARTED WHEN THE BAND BEGAN RECORDING ITS FIRST MAJOR LABEL ALBUM, NEVERMIND. THE ALBUM'S FIRST SINGLE "SMELLS LIKE TEEN SPIRIT" GAINED POPULARITY, DUE TO SIGNIFICANT AIRPLAY OF THE SONG'S MUSIC VIDEO ON MTV.

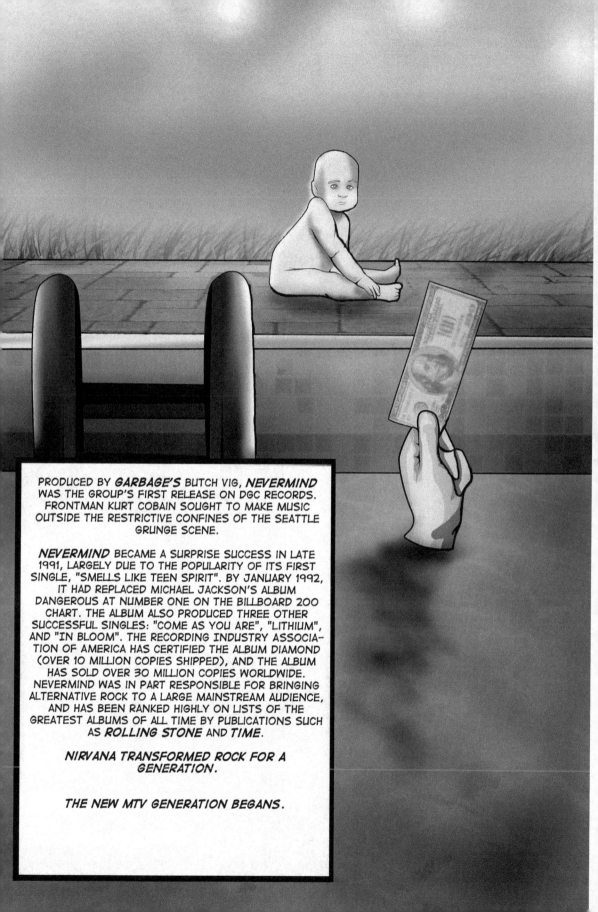

PRODUCED BY **GARBAGE'S** BUTCH VIG, **NEVERMIND** WAS THE GROUP'S FIRST RELEASE ON DGC RECORDS. FRONTMAN KURT COBAIN SOUGHT TO MAKE MUSIC OUTSIDE THE RESTRICTIVE CONFINES OF THE SEATTLE GRUNGE SCENE.

NEVERMIND BECAME A SURPRISE SUCCESS IN LATE 1991, LARGELY DUE TO THE POPULARITY OF ITS FIRST SINGLE, "SMELLS LIKE TEEN SPIRIT". BY JANUARY 1992, IT HAD REPLACED MICHAEL JACKSON'S ALBUM DANGEROUS AT NUMBER ONE ON THE BILLBOARD 200 CHART. THE ALBUM ALSO PRODUCED THREE OTHER SUCCESSFUL SINGLES: "COME AS YOU ARE", "LITHIUM", AND "IN BLOOM". THE RECORDING INDUSTRY ASSOCIA-TION OF AMERICA HAS CERTIFIED THE ALBUM DIAMOND (OVER 10 MILLION COPIES SHIPPED), AND THE ALBUM HAS SOLD OVER 30 MILLION COPIES WORLDWIDE. NEVERMIND WAS IN PART RESPONSIBLE FOR BRINGING ALTERNATIVE ROCK TO A LARGE MAINSTREAM AUDIENCE, AND HAS BEEN RANKED HIGHLY ON LISTS OF THE GREATEST ALBUMS OF ALL TIME BY PUBLICATIONS SUCH AS **ROLLING STONE** AND **TIME**.

NIRVANA TRANSFORMED ROCK FOR A GENERATION.

THE NEW MTV GENERATION BEGANS.

KURT FOUND HIMSELF IN A LOVE-HATE
RELATIONSHIP WITH *COURTNEY LOVE.*
SHE IS AN AMERICAN
SINGER-SONGWRITER, MUSICIAN,
ACTRESS, AND ARTIST.
AS FRONTWOMAN OF ALTERNATIVE
ROCK BAND *HOLE.*
THEY BOTH MET AT THE NIGHTCLUB IN
PORTLAND AND HIT IT OFF WELL.

THEY BOTH DWELLED ON DRUGS.
THE MEDIA CALLED THEM THE JUNKIE COUPLE.
COURTNEY LOVE IS LOUD AND LOVE THE
ROCK AND GLAM ATTENTIONS.
KURT IS JUST THE OPPOSITE OF HER.
BUT THEY HIT IT WELL.
THEY GOT MARRIED.

TRAPPED IN THE FORM OF
HEART-SHAPED BOX
KURT COBAIN BECAME A FATHER TO
FRANCES BEAN COBAIN.

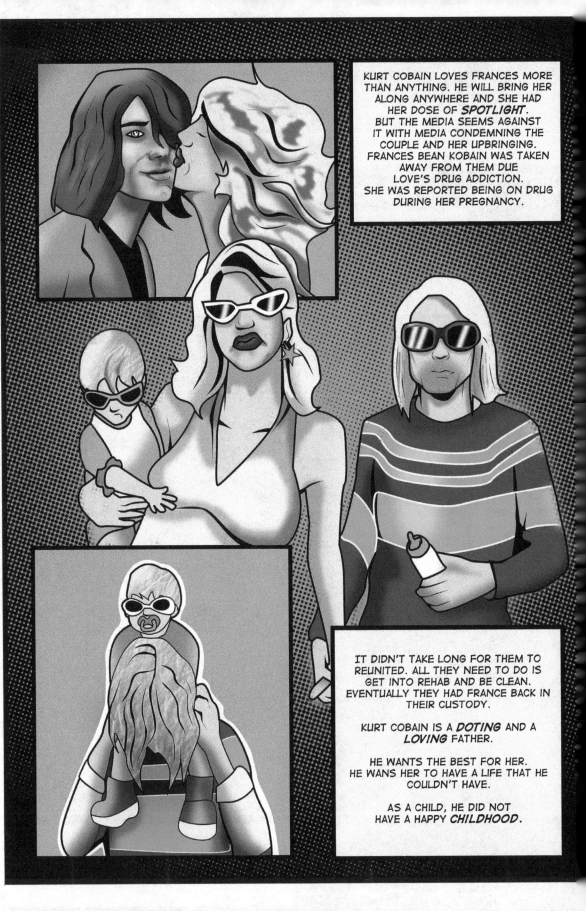

KURT COBAIN LOVES FRANCES MORE THAN ANYTHING. HE WILL BRING HER ALONG ANYWHERE AND SHE HAD HER DOSE OF *SPOTLIGHT*.
BUT THE MEDIA SEEMS AGAINST IT WITH MEDIA CONDEMNING THE COUPLE AND HER UPBRINGING.
FRANCES BEAN KOBAIN WAS TAKEN AWAY FROM THEM DUE LOVE'S DRUG ADDICTION.
SHE WAS REPORTED BEING ON DRUG DURING HER PREGNANCY.

IT DIDN'T TAKE LONG FOR THEM TO REUNITED. ALL THEY NEED TO DO IS GET INTO REHAB AND BE CLEAN. EVENTUALLY THEY HAD FRANCE BACK IN THEIR CUSTODY.

KURT COBAIN IS A *DOTING* AND A *LOVING* FATHER.

HE WANTS THE BEST FOR HER.
HE WANS HER TO HAVE A LIFE THAT HE COULDN'T HAVE.

AS A CHILD, HE DID NOT HAVE A HAPPY *CHILDHOOD*.

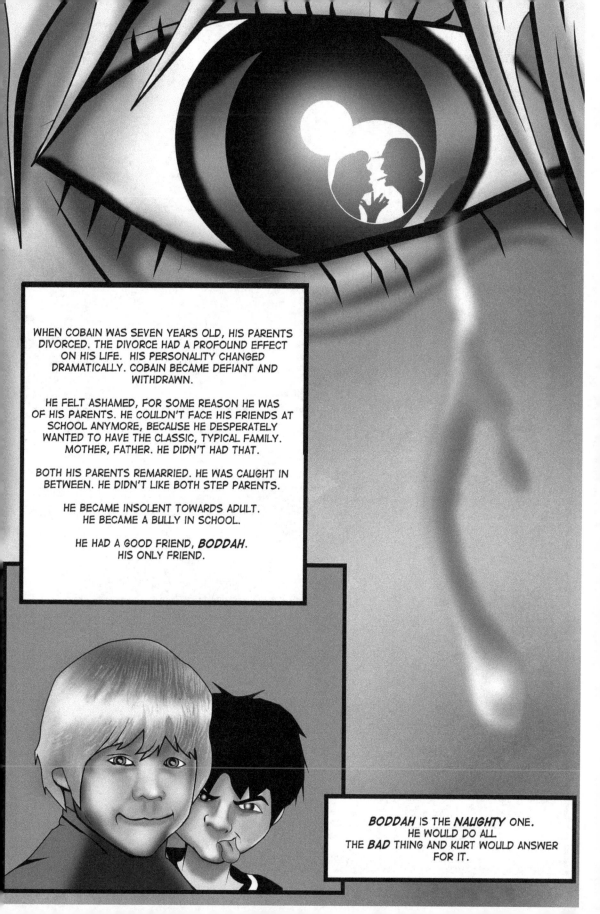

WHEN COBAIN WAS SEVEN YEARS OLD, HIS PARENTS
DIVORCED. THE DIVORCE HAD A PROFOUND EFFECT
ON HIS LIFE. HIS PERSONALITY CHANGED
DRAMATICALLY. COBAIN BECAME DEFIANT AND
WITHDRAWN.

HE FELT ASHAMED, FOR SOME REASON HE WAS
OF HIS PARENTS. HE COULDN'T FACE HIS FRIENDS AT
SCHOOL ANYMORE, BECAUSE HE DESPERATELY
WANTED TO HAVE THE CLASSIC, TYPICAL FAMILY.
MOTHER, FATHER. HE DIDN'T HAD THAT.

BOTH HIS PARENTS REMARRIED. HE WAS CAUGHT IN
BETWEEN. HE DIDN'T LIKE BOTH STEP PARENTS.

HE BECAME INSOLENT TOWARDS ADULT.
HE BECAME A BULLY IN SCHOOL.

HE HAD A GOOD FRIEND, *BODDAH*.
HIS ONLY FRIEND.

BODDAH IS THE *NAUGHTY* ONE.
HE WOULD DO ALL
THE *BAD* THING AND KURT WOULD ANSWER
FOR IT.

IN HIGH SCHOOL, KURT, BEING ECCENTRIC MIXED WITH A HOMOSEXUAL PAL,KURT THOUGHT THAT HE WAS GAY, HE HAD A GAY FRIEND, AND THEN HIS MOTHER WOULDN'T ALLOW HIM TO BE FRIENDS WITH HIM ANYMORE, BECAUSE SHE'S HOMOPHOBIC. HE COULDN'T HANG OUT WITH HIM ANYMORE. BUT KURT IS NOT GAY, IT'S JUST THAT HE LIKES THE IDEA OF PEOPLE IGNORING HIM THINKING HE IS ONE. MAYBE IT'S IN HIS GAY SPIRIT OR MAYBE KURT GREW UP JUST TOTALLY WIERD. HE HATES HOMOPHOBIC.

IN 1992 IN ONE OF THE GIG HE TAKES THE MIC AND SAID "AT THIS POINT I HAVE A REQUEST FOR OUR FANS. IF ANY OF YOU IN ANY WAY HATE HOMOSEXUALS, PEOPLE OF DIFFERENT COLOR, OR WOMEN, PLEASE DO THIS ONE FAVOR FOR US -- LEAVE US ALONE!
DON'T COME TO OUR SHOWS AND DON'T BUY OUR RECORDS."

KURT ONCE WORKED AS A JANITOR AND AT ONE TIME HE DID A GRAFFITI ON A BUILDING WALL AND DIDN'T KNOW HIS JOB REQUIRE HIM TO CLEAN IT UP THE NEXT DAY.
HE ALMOST JOINED THE NAVY.

A BLESSING OR A CURSE
KURT COBAIN
BECAME A ROCK ICON.

IN *1993*, NIRVANA EMBARKED ON
ITS FIRST TOUR OF THE UNITED STATES AFTER THE
RELEASED OF THE ALBUM '*IN UTERO*'.
ALTERNATIVE MUSIC WAS
CONSIGNED TO SPECIALTY SECTIONS OF RECORD
STORES.

NIRVANA STARTED A ROCK REVOLUTION"
AND REMAIN AN ENDURING INFLUENCE AND THAT
THEY WERE THE RIGHT BAND WITH THE RIGHT NOISE
AND COULD CHANGE THE WORLD.

ONLY A FEW BANDS IN ROCK HISTORY HAVE HAD A
MORE IMMEDIATE AND TANGIBLE IMPACT ON THEIR
CONTEMPORARY POP MUSICAL LANDSCAPE THAN
NIRVANA .

THEY WERE THE *GRUNGE GODS* OF ALTERNATIVE
MUSIC.

AND THAT IS PRESSURING AND IT'S LONELY
BEING AT THE *TOP*.

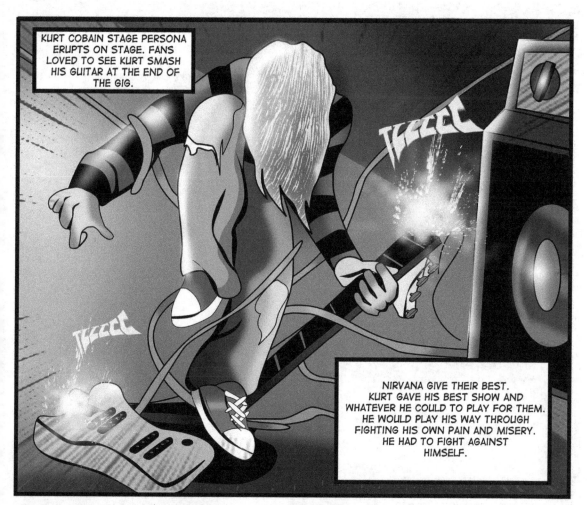

KURT COBAIN STAGE PERSONA ERUPTS ON STAGE. FANS LOVED TO SEE KURT SMASH HIS GUITAR AT THE END OF THE GIG.

NIRVANA GIVE THEIR BEST. KURT GAVE HIS BEST SHOW AND WHATEVER HE COULD TO PLAY FOR THEM. HE WOULD PLAY HIS WAY THROUGH FIGHTING HIS OWN PAIN AND MISERY. HE HAD TO FIGHT AGAINST HIMSELF.

You doin okay Kurt? we can shortened the setlist.

I am dying for goodness sake! This pain is killing me!!! It's all over me. I am DeaD!

NOONE KNOWS HIS PAIN. KURT COBAIN COULD NOT FIGHT HIS ILLNESS.

KURT COBAIN GOT INTO A BAD STATE.

EXIT

COBAIN SUFFERED FROM *CHRONIC BRONCHITIS* AND INTENSE PHYSICAL PAIN DUE TO AN UNDIAGNOSED *CHRONIC STOMACH CONDITION*. HE OFTEN VOMITTED DURING SHOWS UNCONTROLLABLY. ONE DAY, COBAIN WAS DIAGNOSED WITH *BRONCHITIS* AND SEVERE *LARYNGITIS*. HE FLEW TO ROME THE NEXT DAY FOR MEDICAL TREATMENT, THEN JOINED BY BY COURTNEY LOVE. THE NEXT MORNING, LOVE AWOKE TO FIND THAT COBAIN HAD OVERDOSED ON A COMBINATION OF *CHAMPAGNE* AND *ROHYPNOL*. COBAIN WAS IMMEDIATELY RUSHED TO THE HOSPITAL, AND SPENT THE REST OF THE DAY UNCONSCIOUS. IT WAS COBAIN'S FIRST SUICIDE ATTEMPT. HE IS *SUICIDAL*.

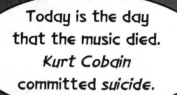

Today is the day
that the music died.
Kurt Cobain
committed *suicide.*

NIRVANA WAS SET TO HEADLINE *1994'S LOLLAPALOOZA,* THE
ALTERNATIVE ROCK FEST OF THAT ERA. *NIRVANA* NEVER PERFORMED.
KURT COBAIN WAS *MISSING.* NOONE KNEW WHERE HE WAS.

ON *APRIL 8, 1994,* KURT COBAIN AGED *27* WAS FOUND DEADN HIS BODY
WAS DISCOVERED AT HIS LAKE WASHINGTON HOME BY AN ELECTRICIAN
WHO CAMED TO INSTALL A SECURITY SYSTEM.

COBAIN'S BODY HAD BEEN LYING THERE FOR DAYS; THE CORONER'S REPORT
ESTIMATED COBAIN TO HAVE DIED ON *APRIL 5, 1994.*

A SHOTGUN NEXT TO HIM.

DO NOT CROSS

KURT LEFT BEHIND HIS WIFE, DAUGHTER, FRIENDS AND FAMILIES.

AND A CONTROVERSIAL SUICIDE NOTE FOR *BODDAH*.

SEEMS TRAGIC
ON HOW MEDIA SELLS IT,
BUT KURT COBAIN
IS IN A BETTER PLACE.
HE IS IN *NIRVANA*.

TIDALWAVE
COMICS

Mike Lynch, Michael L. Frizell, Jayfri HashimScott Davis — Writer

George Amaru, Jayfri Hashim, Manuel Díaz — Penciler

Jayfri Hashim & Eva — Colorist

David Hopkins & Gary Scott Beatty — Letterer

Graham Hill — Cover

Darren G. Davis
Publisher

Maggie Jessup
Publicity

Susan Ferris
Entertainment Manager